THE SECRET LIFE OF PETS

Popcorn ELT Readers

Meet ...
everyone from

THE SECRET LIFE OF PETS

Max and his friends live in New York City.

Max lives with Katie.

Katie

Max

He goes to the park with the dog walker.

Duke

Gidget

Chloe

Max's home is next to the Hudson River and the Brooklyn Bridge.

bridge

river

Animal Control look for dogs in the city. They put the dogs in cages.

Snowball the rabbit

Snowball and Ripper live in the sewer. Ozone lives in a bin.

Ripper

Ozone

Before you read ...
Katie goes out in the day. What does Max do?

New Words

What do these new words mean? Ask your teacher or use your dictionary.

cage

It is in a **cage**.

bin

This is a **bin**.

help

He is **helping** his mother.

break

My pencils always **break**!

idea

I have an **idea**!

jump

I'm **jumping**!

key

This is a **key**.

pet

I've got a lot of **pets**!

sewer

There are **sewers** under the city.

van

This **van** is blue.

'Life is good!'

Life is good!

What does the title *The Secret Life of Pets* mean? Ask your teacher.

CHAPTER ONE
Max and Katie

Max loves Katie. Katie loves Max. They walk in the park. They play with a ball. Life is good!

Katie goes out in the mornings. What does Max do all day? He sits at the door. He talks to his friends, Gidget and Chloe.

At six o'clock, Katie comes home! Max loves
six o'clock! But today Katie has a new dog
with her. His name is Duke. He has no home.

Duke sleeps in Max's bed. Max is sad.

In the morning, Katie goes out. Duke eats Max's food.

Max has an idea. 'One: I break Katie's picture and the table!' he thinks. 'Two: Katie comes home and says, "Oh no! Duke is bad." Three: Duke goes away. Yes!'

CHAPTER TWO
Max and Duke

The dog walker goes to the park with Max, Duke and six more dogs.

'Max doesn't like me,' Duke thinks. 'But I want to live with Katie.'

Then Duke has an idea. 'One: Run out of the park. Two: Put Max in a bin. Yes!'

But there is a cat in the bin. His name is Ozone. And now Ozone is angry!

Ozone and his friends run after Max and Duke. But then Animal Control see the two dogs. They put Max and Duke in a cage.

CHAPTER THREE
Snowball

'Help!' Max shouts.
Suddenly the Animal Control van stops. An angry rabbit jumps onto the van.
 'I'm Snowball!' he says.

There is a dog in the cage next to Max and Duke. Snowball opens the dog's cage.

'Let's go, Ripper!' he says.

Then he opens Max and Duke's cage.

'Come with me!' he shouts.

Snowball lives in the sewer. A lot of animals live in the sewer.

'Say hi to two new friends!' Snowball says to the sewer animals.

'They're not friends!' someone shouts. It is Ozone. 'They're pets!'

The sewer animals are angry. 'We don't like pets!' they shout. 'Pets have homes!'

The sewer animals run after Max and Duke. Max and Duke jump into the river.

CHAPTER FOUR
Gidget

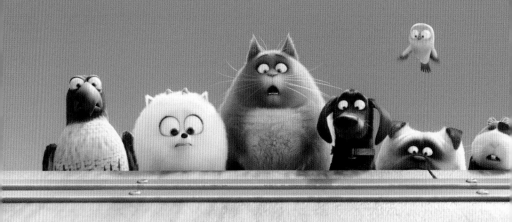

Gidget sees the dog walker. He has six dogs.

'Where are Max and Duke?' Gidget shouts.
'Look in the city! Look in the river! Look on the bridge!'

'We're coming!' her friends say.

Max and Duke are in Brooklyn. But Animal Control see Duke again.

'Run away!' Duke shouts to Max.

They put Duke in the van. There is a dog in the cage next to Duke.

'You again!' Duke says. It is Ripper.

Snowball sees Max.

'Ripper's in the van,' Snowball says.

'Duke is too!' Max says.

'Go after the van!' Snowball shouts.

The van is on the bridge. Max and Snowball go after the van in a bus.

'Go more slowly!' Max shouts to Snowball.

CRASH!

Animal Control jump out. Their van goes into the river.

Ripper's cage opens and he jumps out.

Duke can't open his cage. And the van is under the water.

'Duke!' Max shouts. 'I'm coming!'

But the sewer animals are on the bridge.

'Stop!' they shout. 'We don't like pets!'

'No! YOU stop!' someone shouts.

'It's Gidget!' Max says.

Gidget and her friends jump on the sewer animals.

'Run, Max!' Gidget shouts.

CHAPTER FIVE
Good friends

Snowball sees the key to the cage. He gives the key to Max. Max jumps into the water and helps Duke.

'Thank you, Max!' Duke says.

It is six o'clock. Max and Duke sit at the door. They are good friends now!

'Hello, boys,' Katie says.
Life is good again!

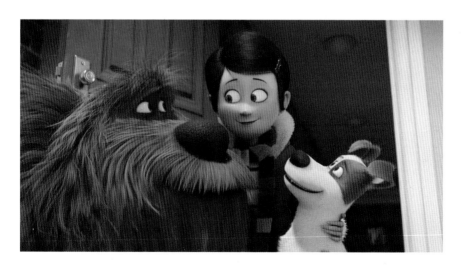

THE END

Real World

WILD in NEW YORK CITY

There are a lot of pets in New York City. Many wild animals and birds live here too.

Hudson River

NEW YORK CITY

Central Park

Skunks in the park

- Skunks come out at night.
- They look for food in bins.
- They can make a horrible smell!

Seahorses in the river

- You can see seahorses under Brooklyn Bridge.
- They can live for four years.
- The seahorses are from 7 cm to 17 cm long.

Hawks in the city

- Hawks live on skyscrapers.
- They eat rats and small animals.

Alligators in the sewers

People from New York say, 'Alligators live in the sewers under the city.' Is it true?

★ Which wild animals live near you? ★

What do these words mean? Find out.

wild   smell   skyscraper
rat   people

After you read

1 Who says this? Write the names.

~~Duke~~ Gidget Katie Max Ozone Snowball

a) 'Thank you, Max!   ....Duke....

b) 'Now I have two dogs!'   ....

c) 'It's my bed!'   ....

d) 'This is my bin!'   ....

e) 'Look on the bridge!'   ....

f) 'Ripper's in the van.'   ....

2 Make sentences.

a) Ozone lives   **i)** to find Max and Duke.

b) Snowball lives   **ii)** in a bin.

c) The sewer animals   **iii)** Katie goes out.

d) Gidget wants   **iv)** don't like pets.

e) Animal Control put   **v)** in the sewer.

f) In the mornings,   **vi)** Duke in a cage.

Where's the popcorn?
Look in your book.
Can you find it?

Puzzle time!

1 What is this?

a) ...... a cat ......

b) ....

c) ....

d) ....

2 Read and tick (✓).

a) Gidget is ...

a white cat. ☐   a white dog. ✓

b) Duke is ...

a big dog. ☐   a small dog. ☐

c) Snowball is ...

a white cat. ☐   a white rabbit. ☐

d) Ozone lives ...

in a bin. ☐   in a home. ☐

e) Max likes ...

the park. ☐   the sewers. ☐

3 Write the words.

p a r k

_ _ _ _ _

_ _ _ _ _ _

_ _ _ _ _

4 Draw your favourite character from the story. Then write a sentence.

I like .... because ....

....

1 Look in your book and find the picture for this dialogue.

Duke	That's a nice bed!
Max	It's MY bed.
Duke	I want to sleep in it too.
Max	No. It's not a very big bed.
Duke	Please!
Max	NO!
Duke	Let's see.
Max	Oh dear!

2 Work with a friend and act out the dialogue.

1 🎧 Listen and read.

Max and Duke

Max loves Katie
But life is very bad.
Katie has a new dog
And Max is very sad.

The pets are in the city.
Snowball's there too.
Now Duke is in the water.
What can Max do?

Max jumps in the water.
He helps his big friend.
'Thank you, Max!' says Duke
And that's a happy end.

2 🎧 Say the chant.